Puzzles

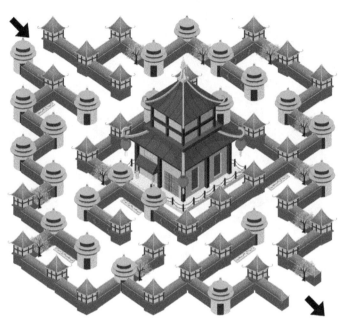

Find your way through

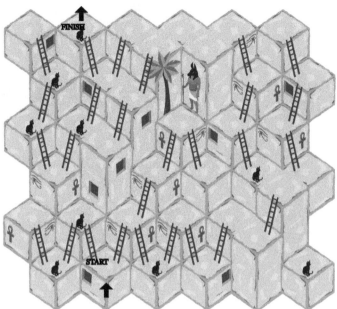

Climb the ladders

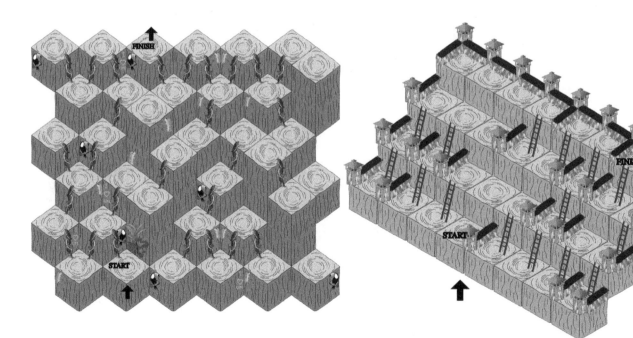

Climb the vines

Get to the top of the stairs

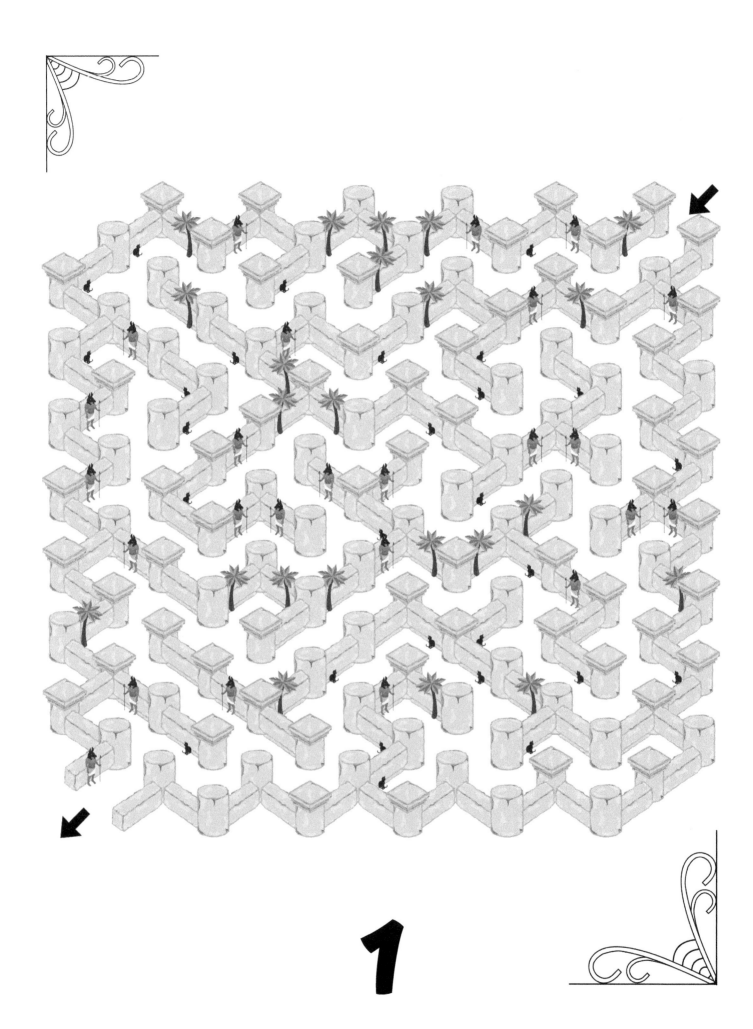

1

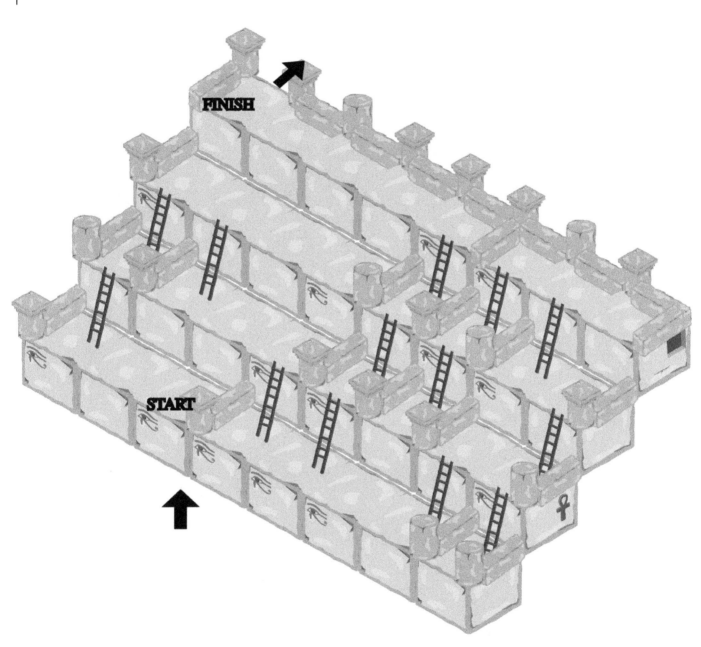

FINISH

START

2

FINISH

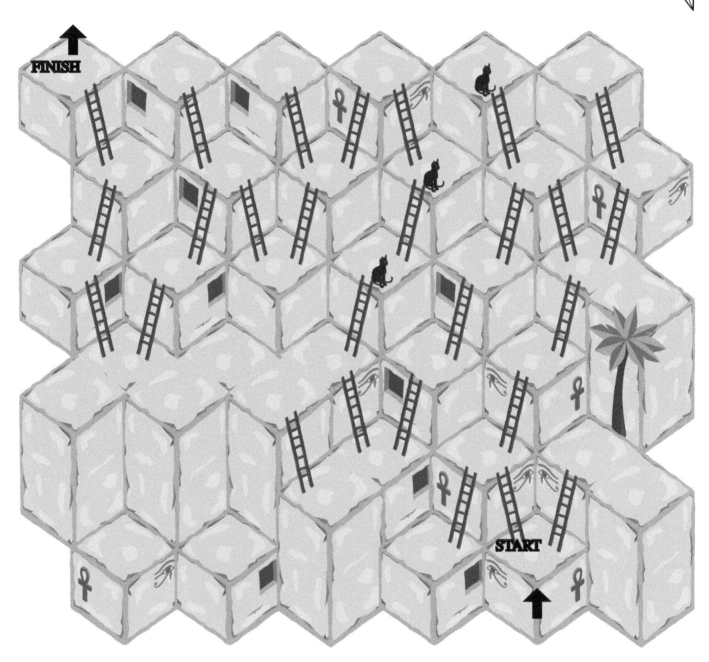

START

3

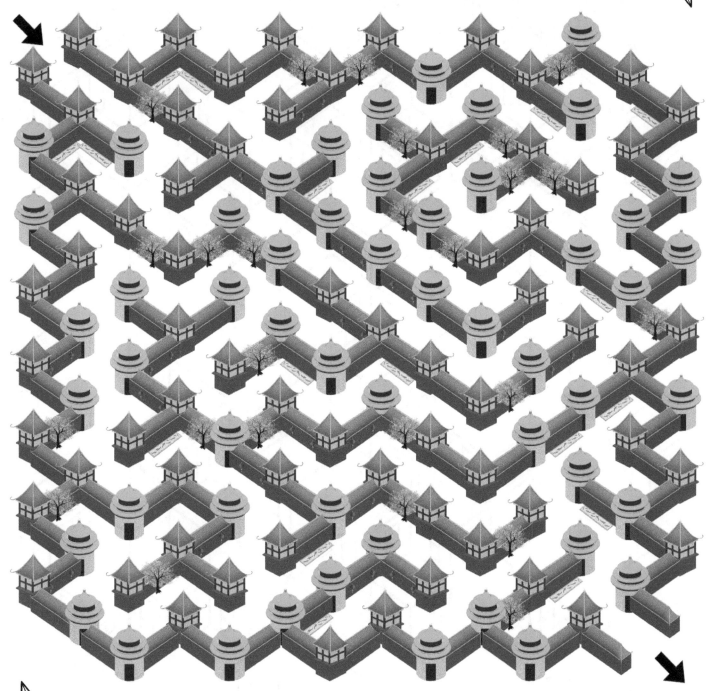

4

FINISH

START

5

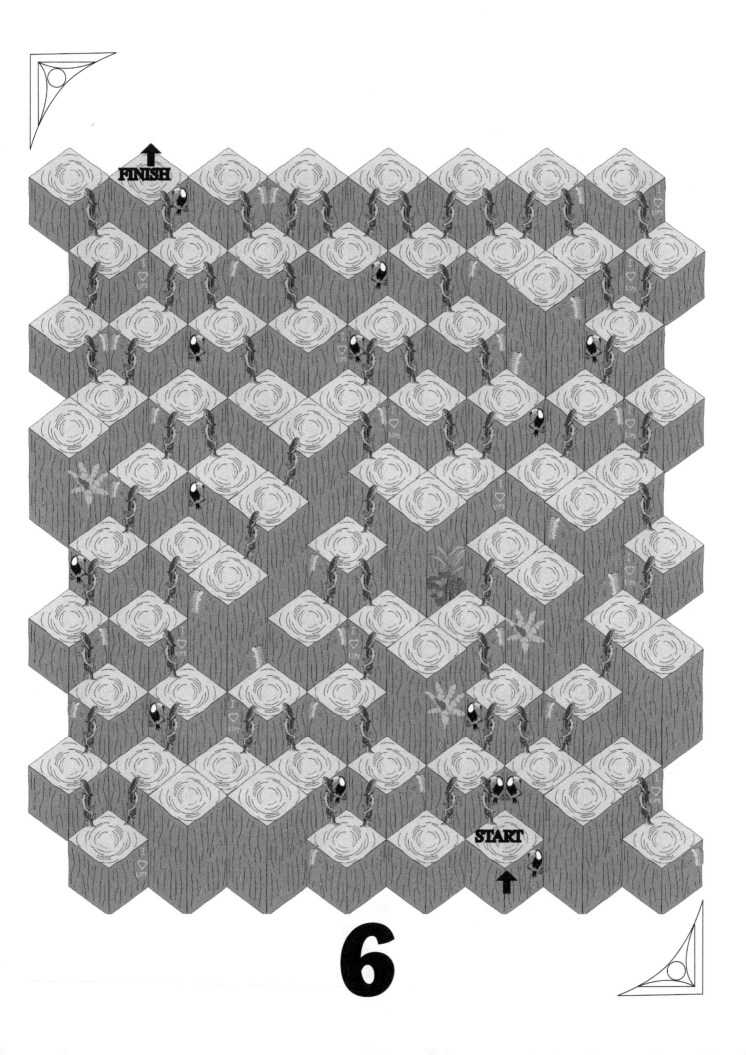

FINISH

START

6

FINISH

START

7

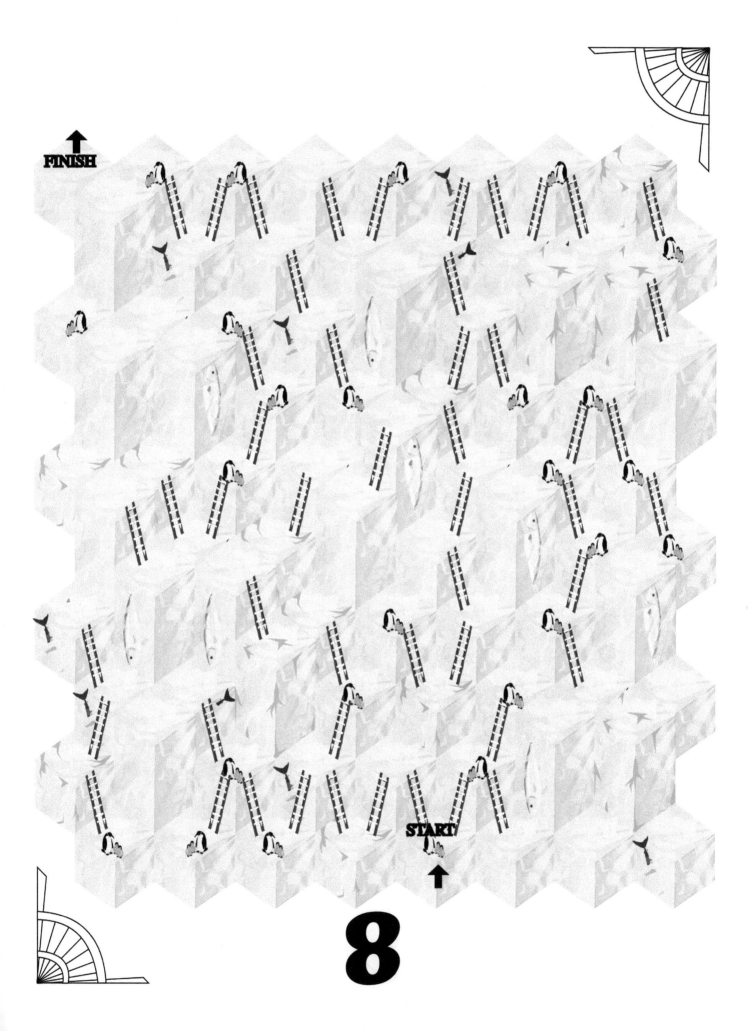

FINISH

START

8

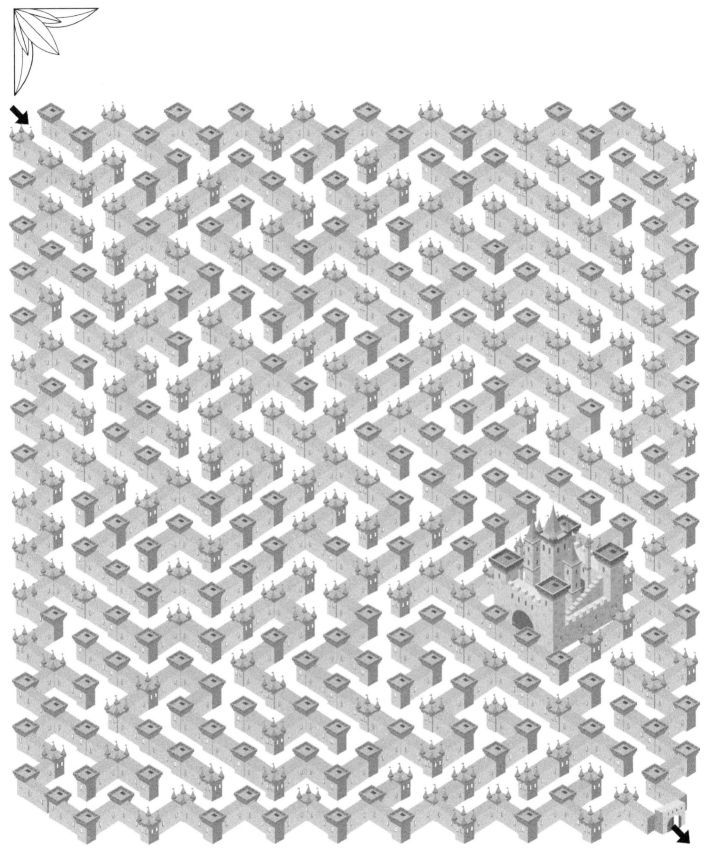

9

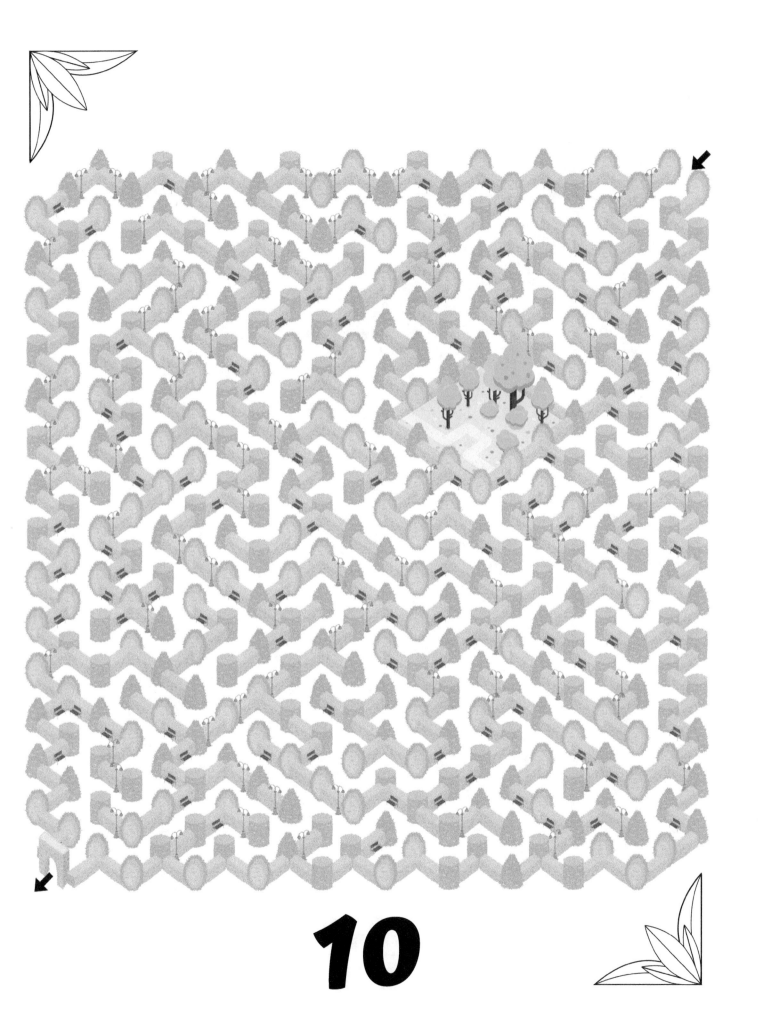

10

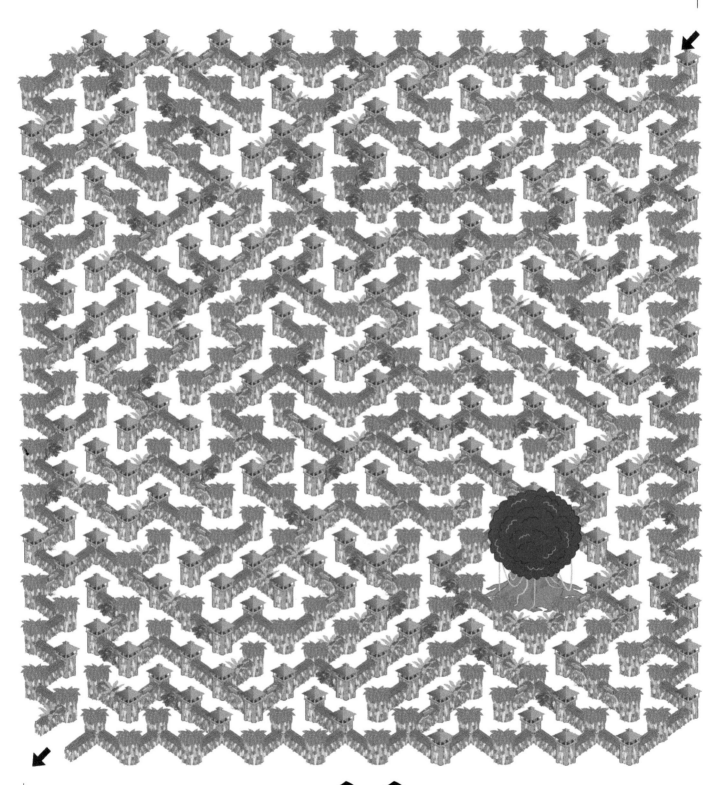

11

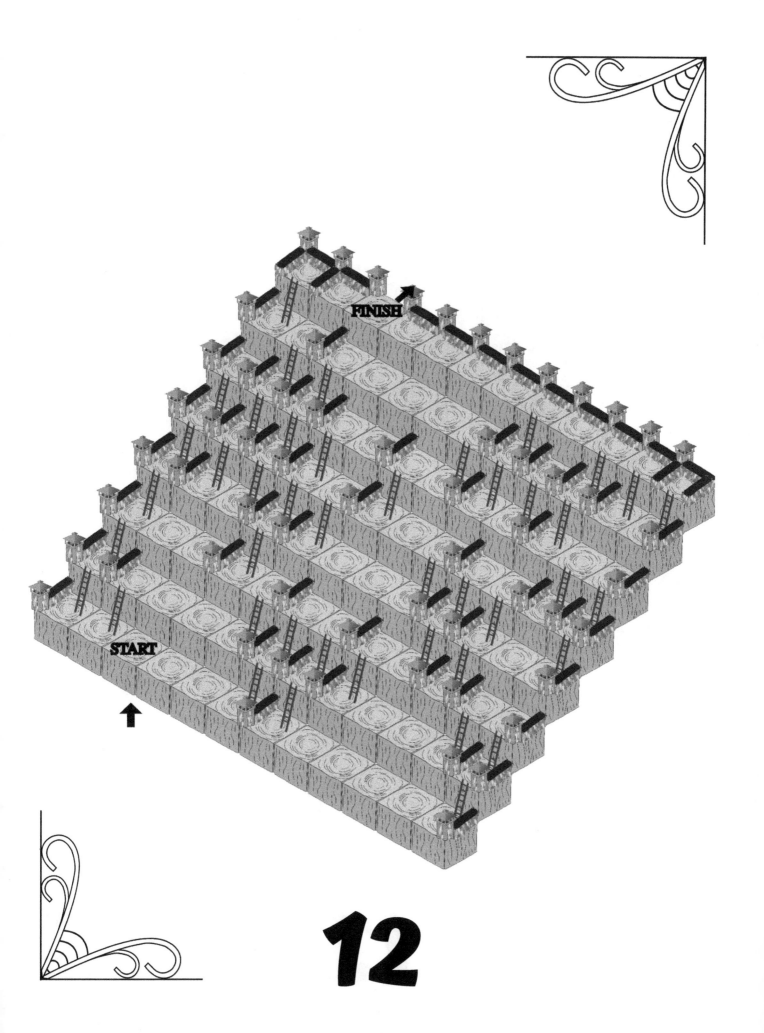

12

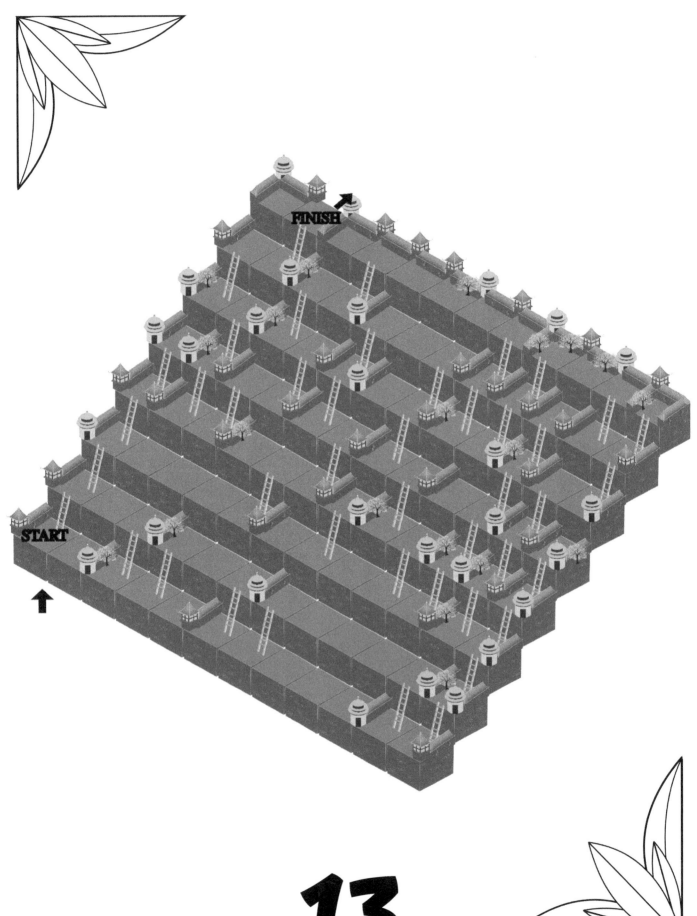

13

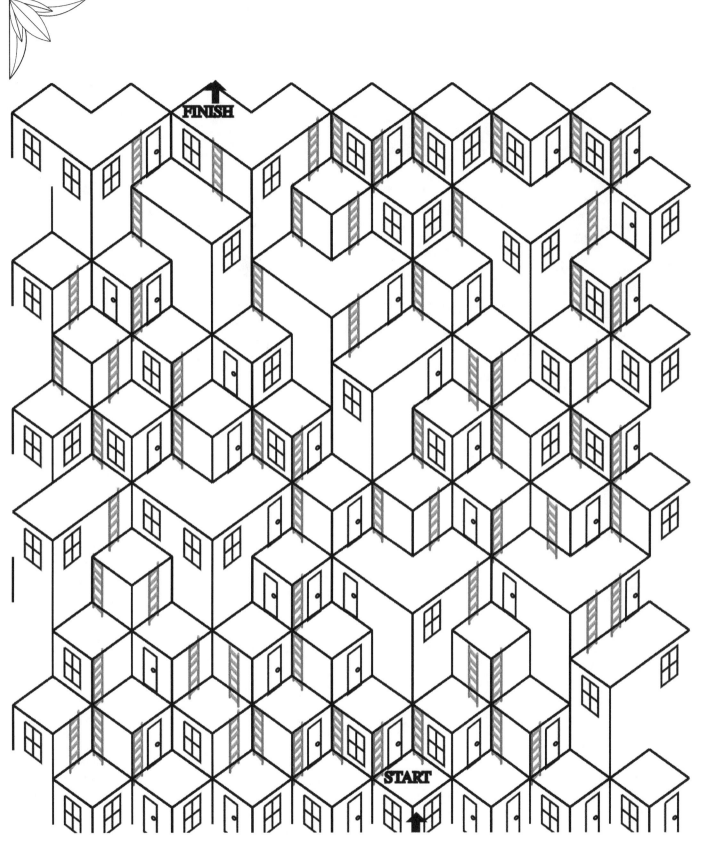

FINISH

START

14

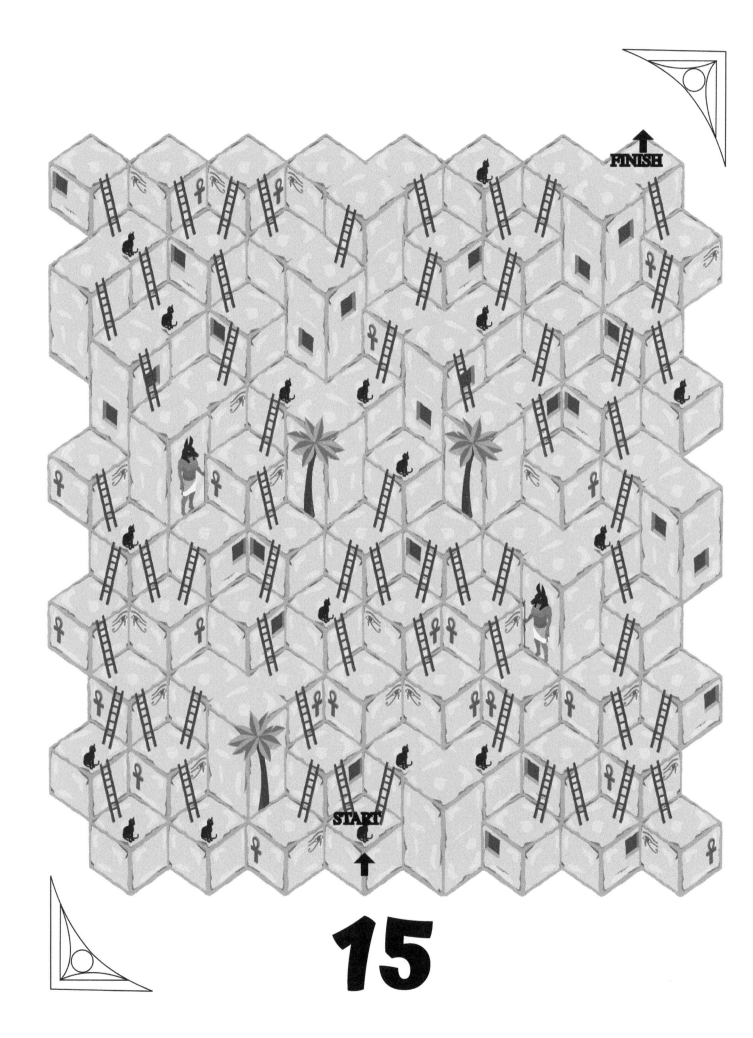

FINISH

START

15

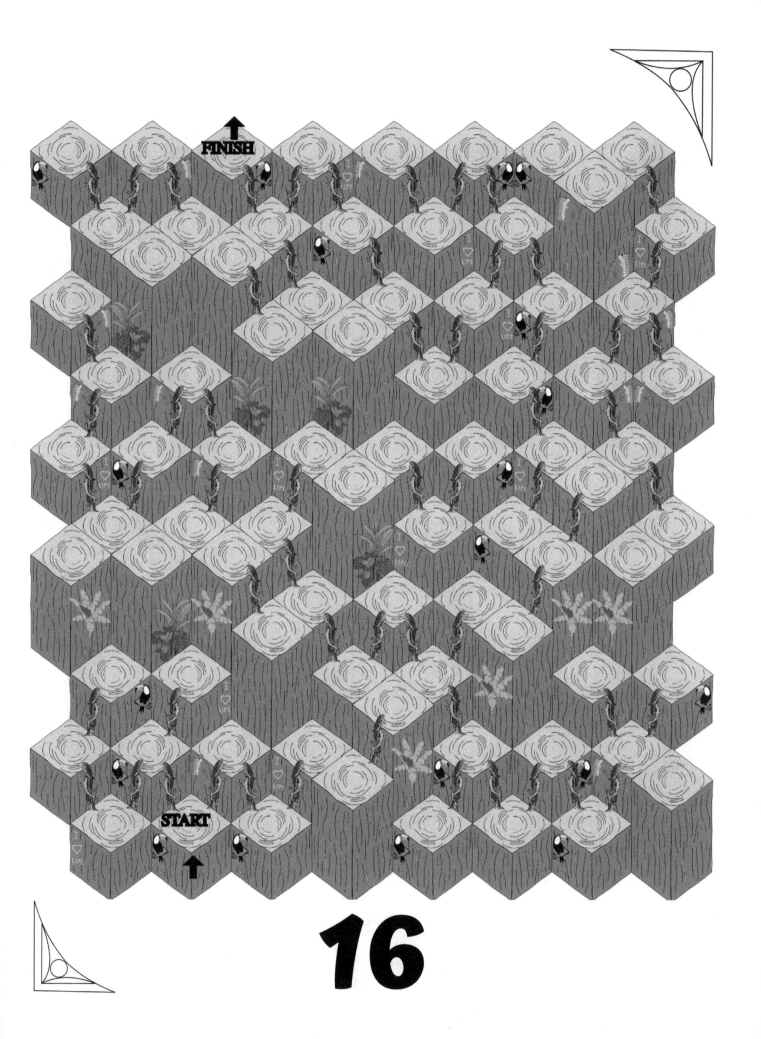

FINISH

START

16

FINISH

START

17

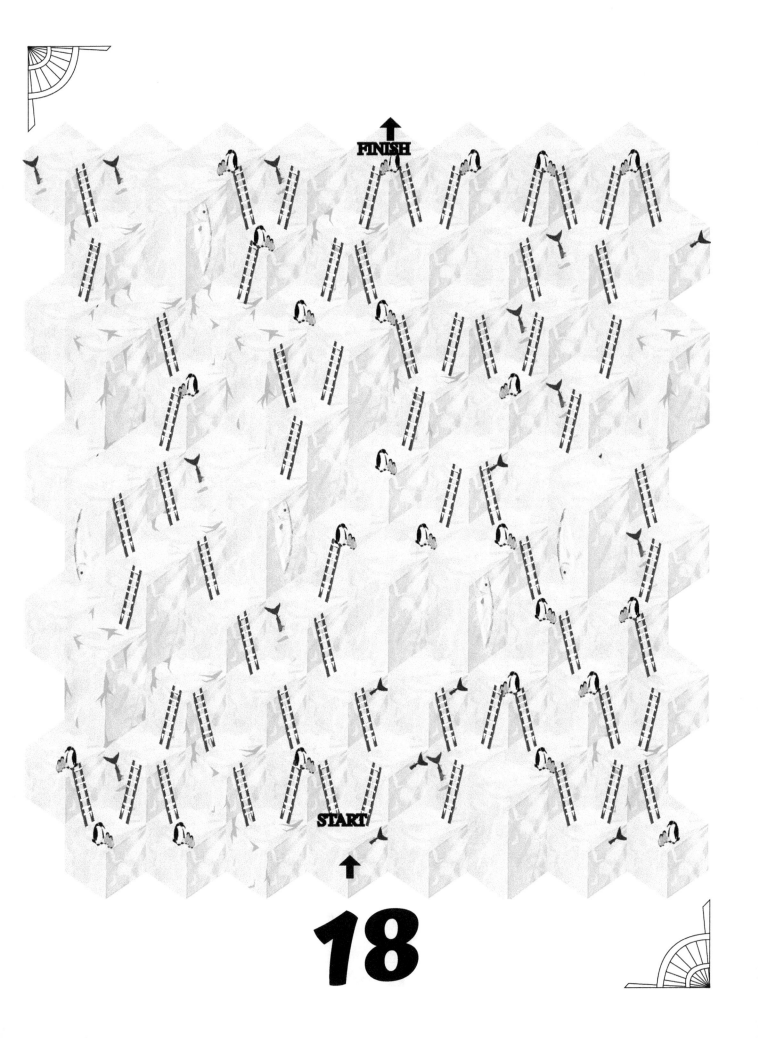

19

20

21

22

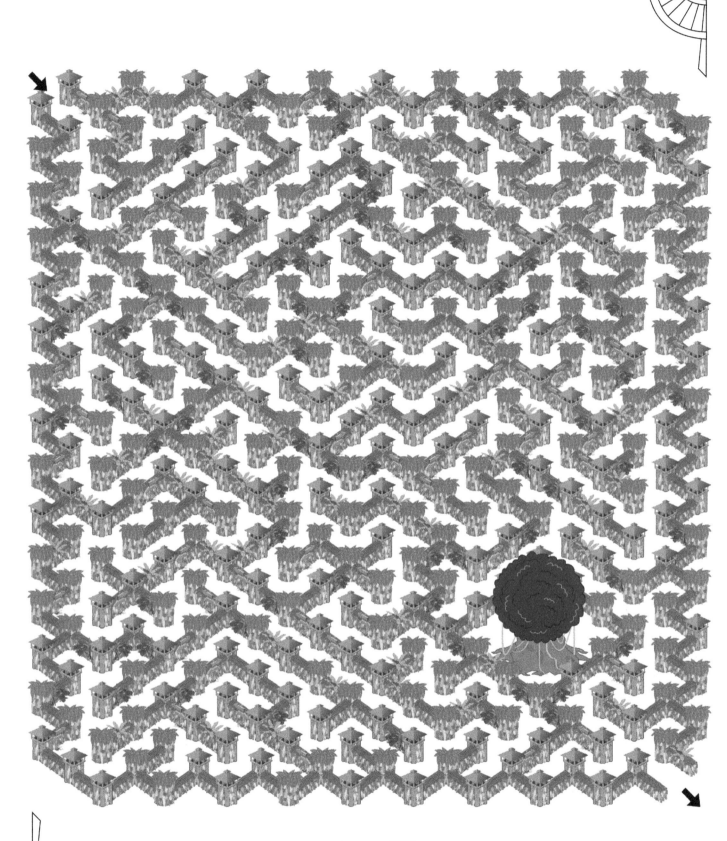

23

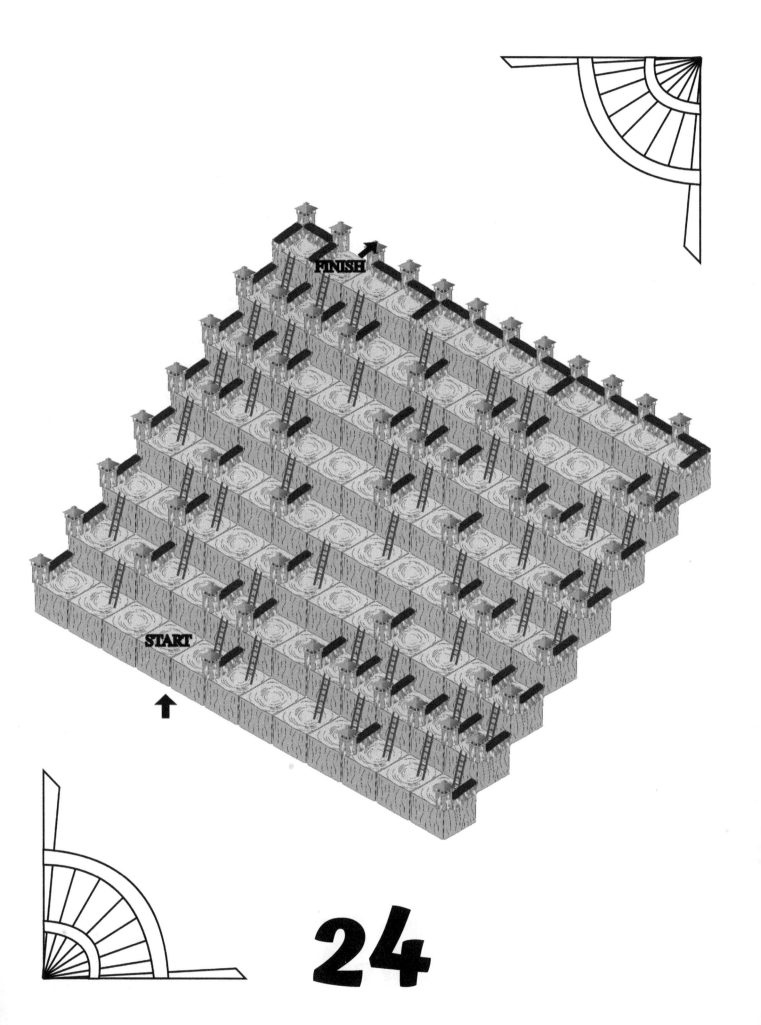

FINISH

START

24

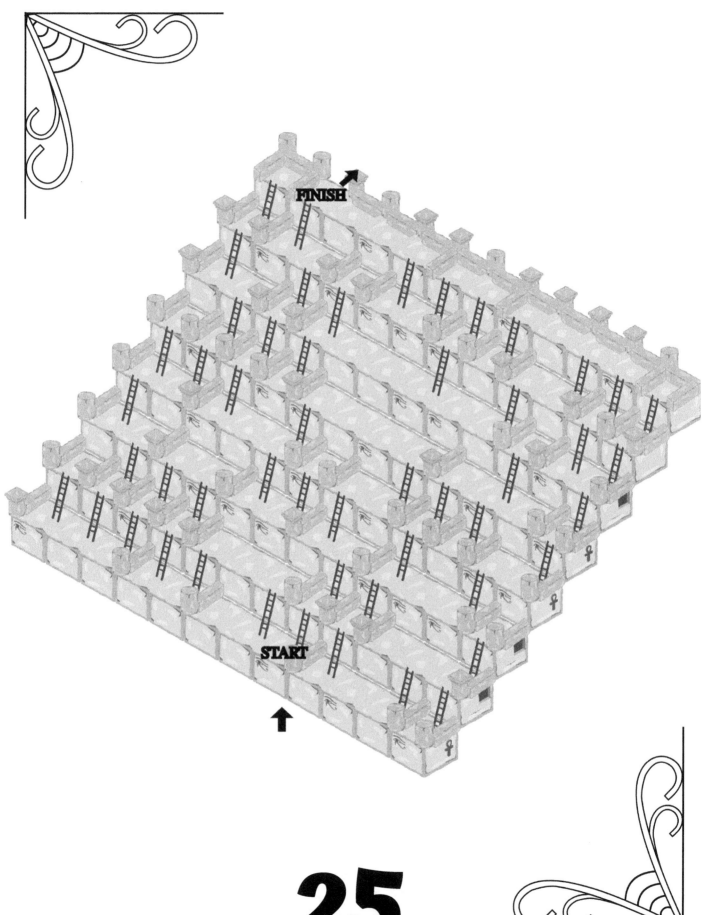

FINISH

START

25

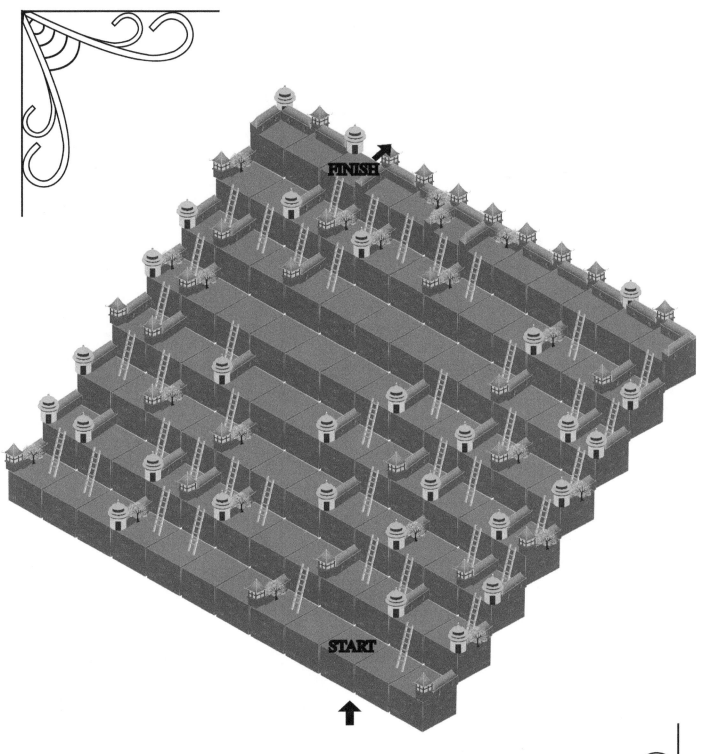

FINISH

START

26

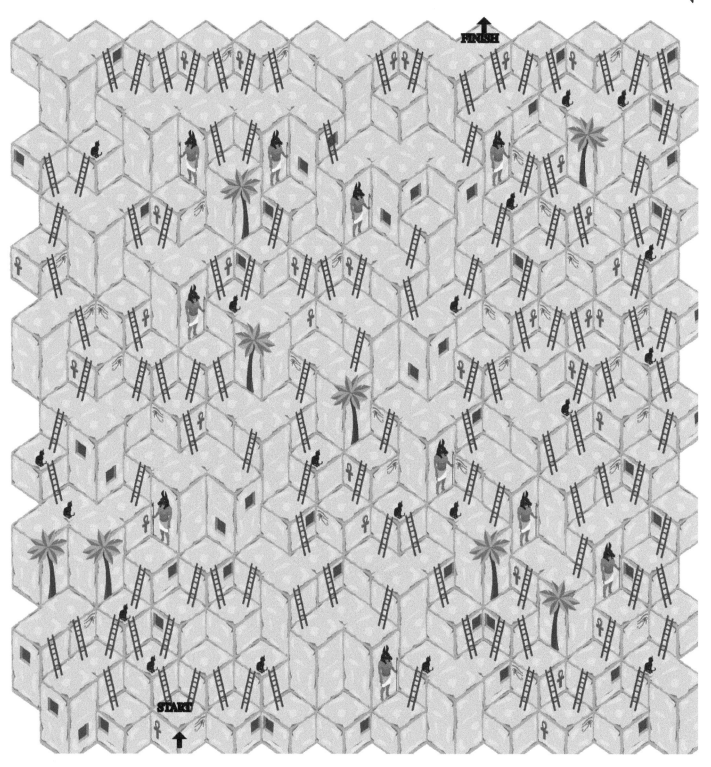

27

28

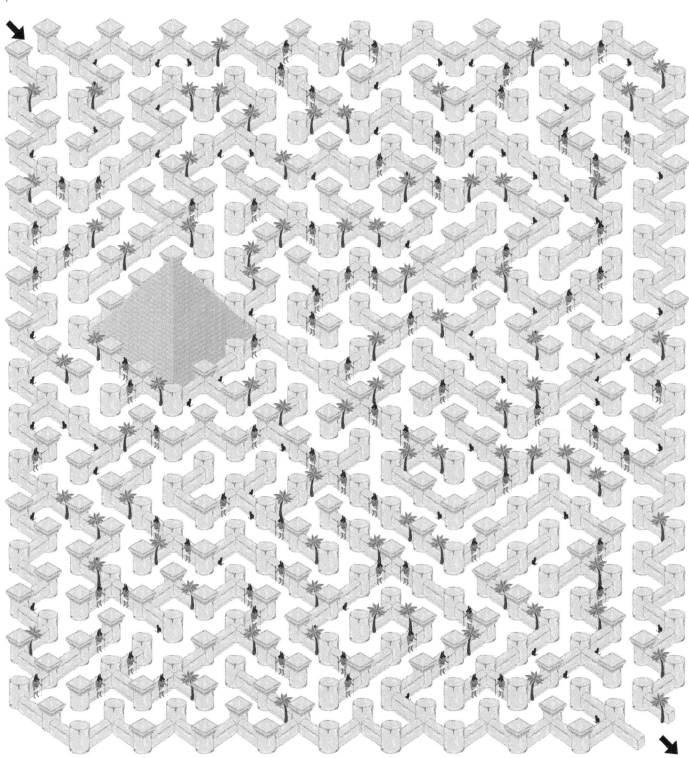

29

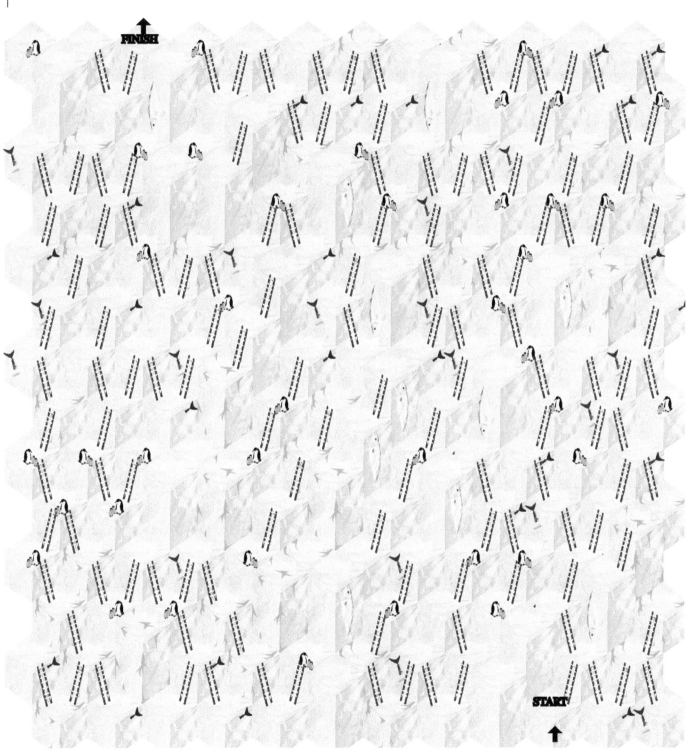

30

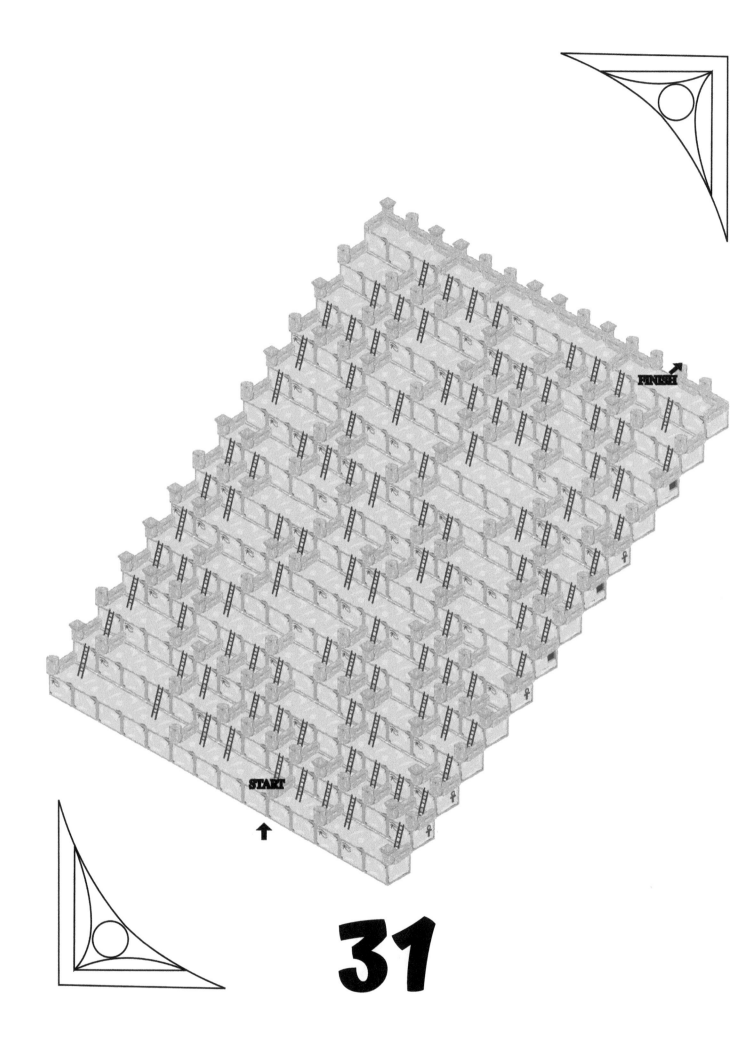

START

FINISH

31

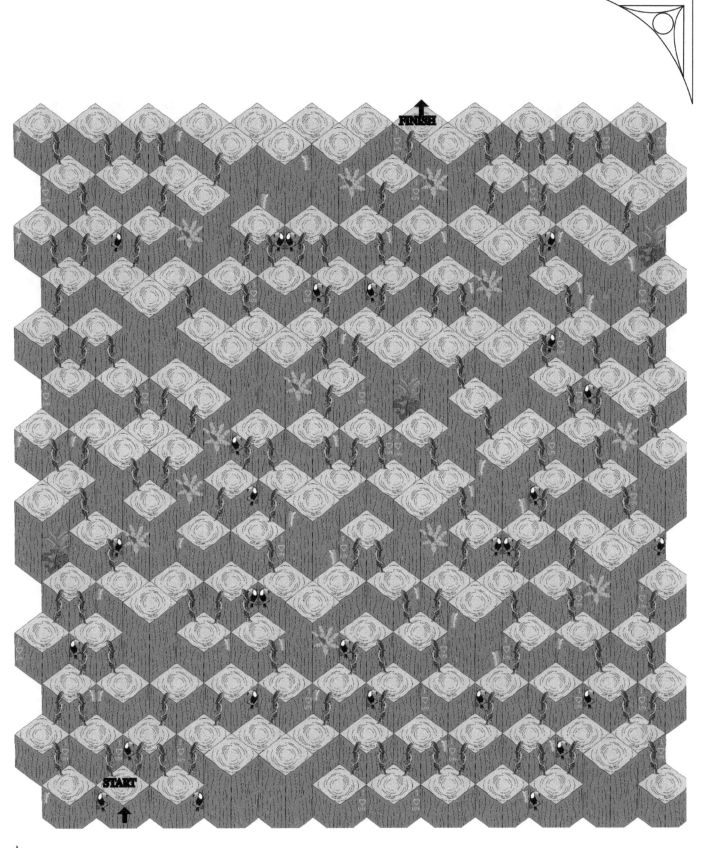

FINISH

START

32

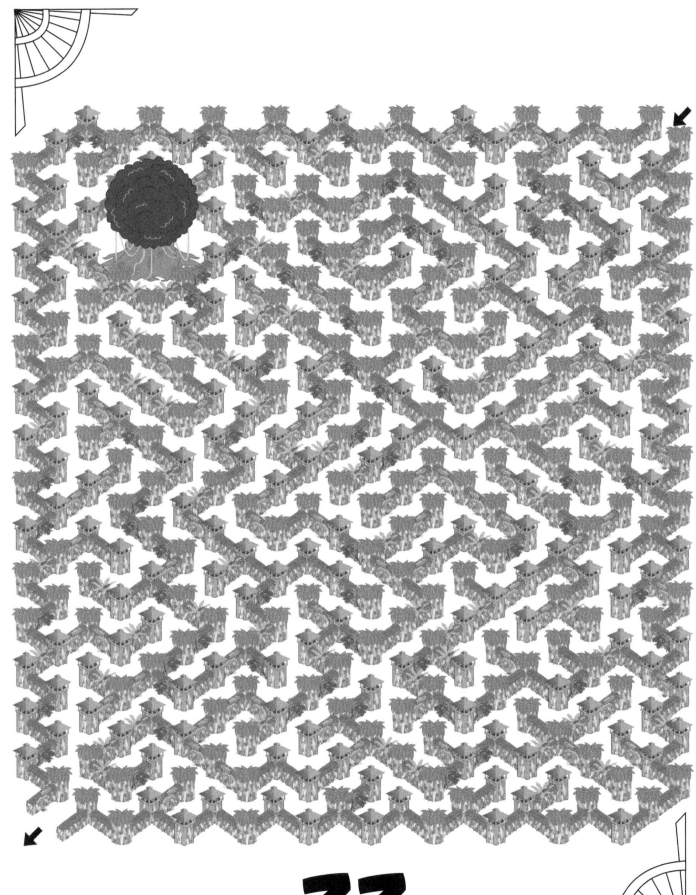

33

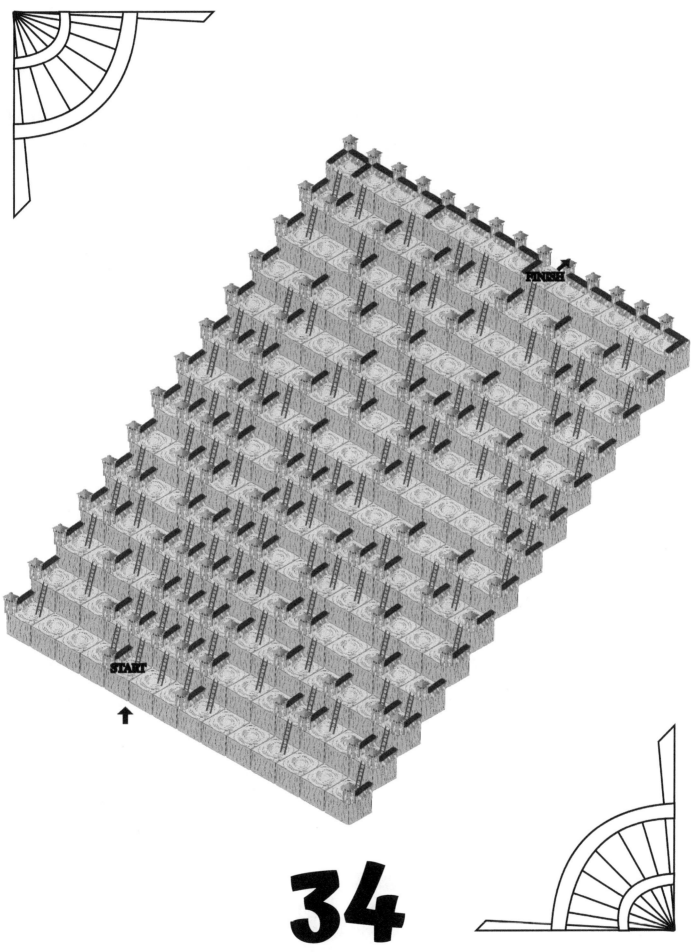

START

FINISH

34

35

36

Solutions

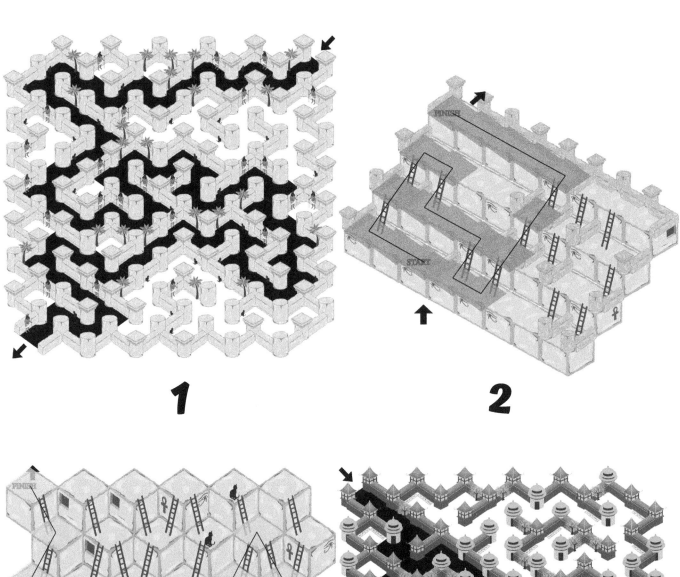

1

2

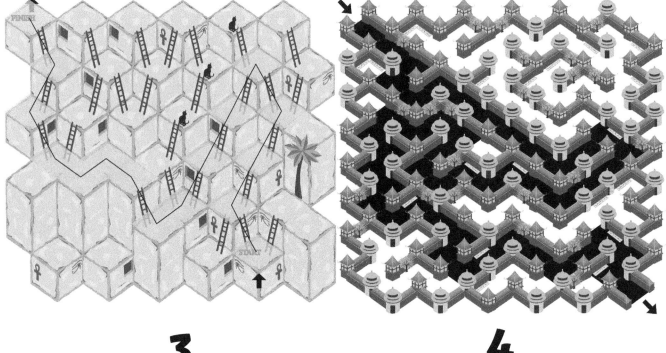

3

4

Solutions

5

6

7

8

Solutions

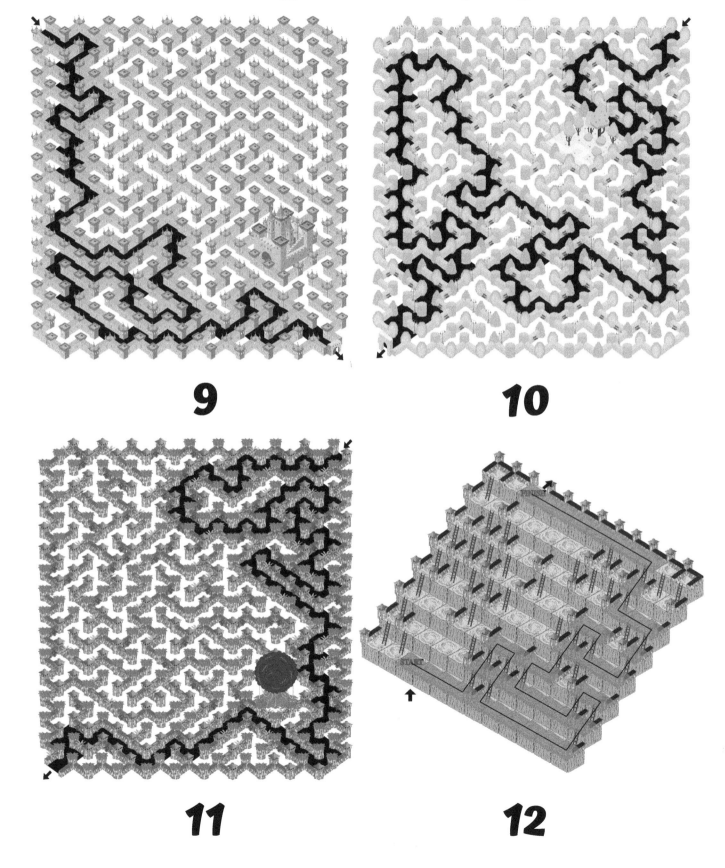

9

10

11

12

Solutions

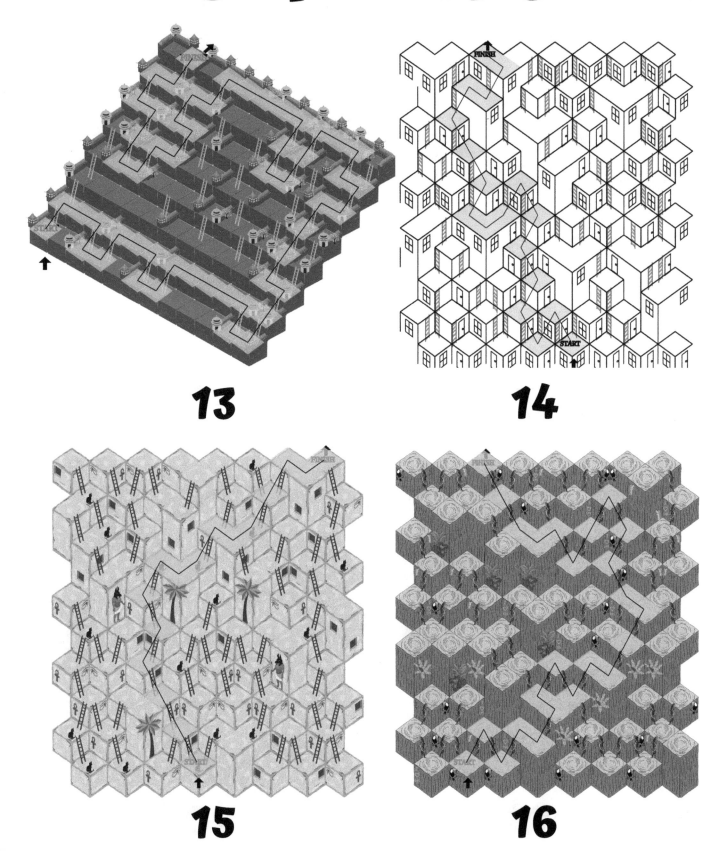

13

14

15

16

Solutions

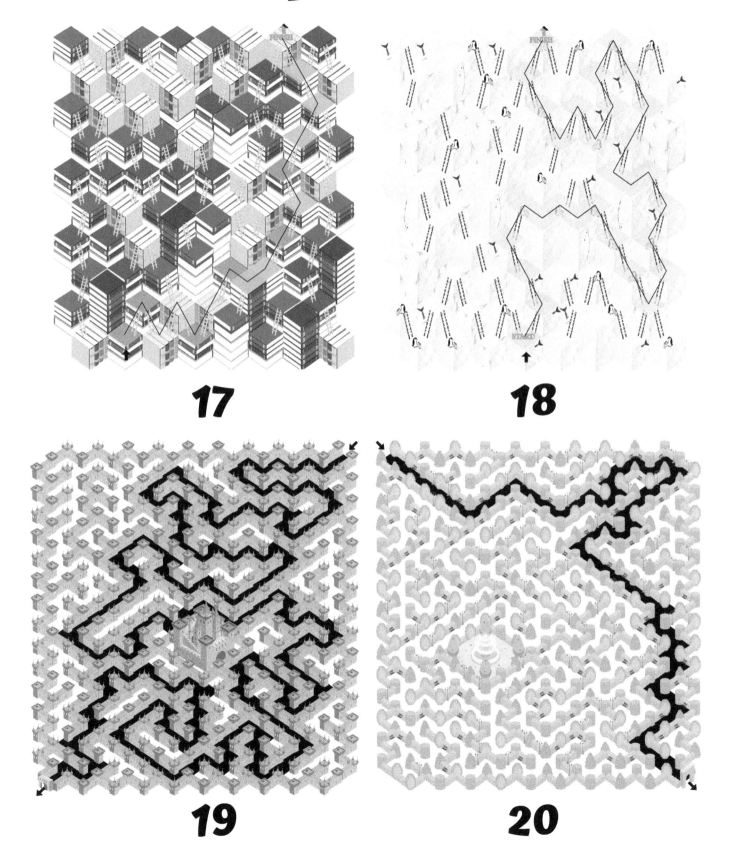

17

18

19

20

Solutions

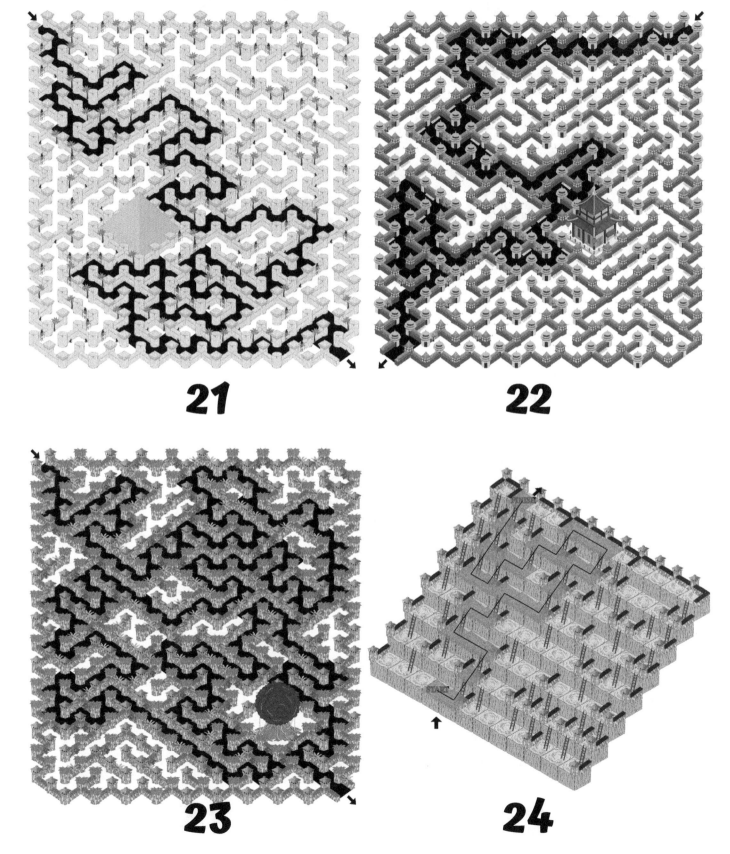

21

22

23

24

Solutions

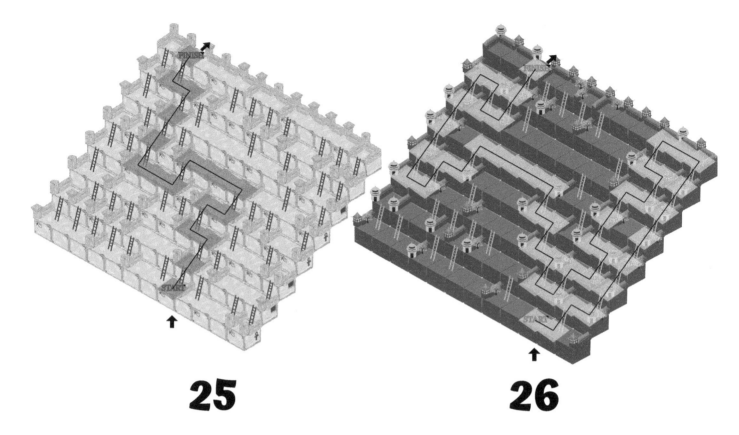

25

26

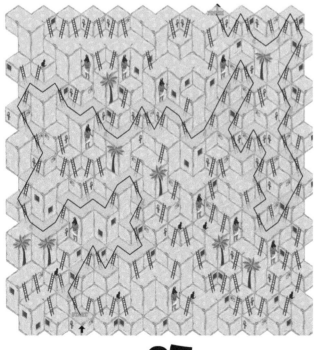

27

28

Solutions

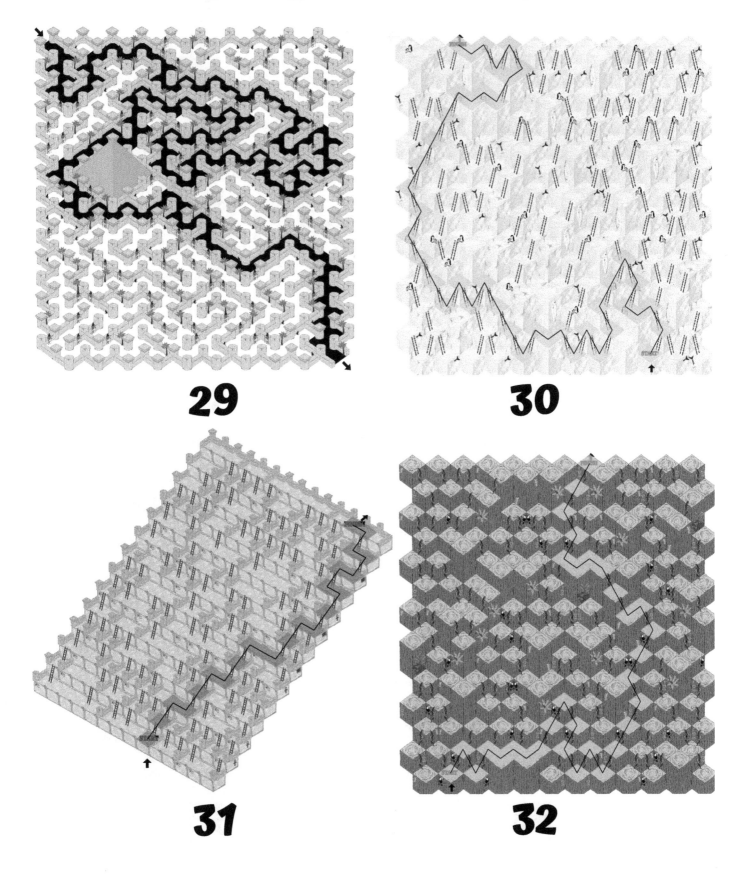

29

30

31

32

Solutions

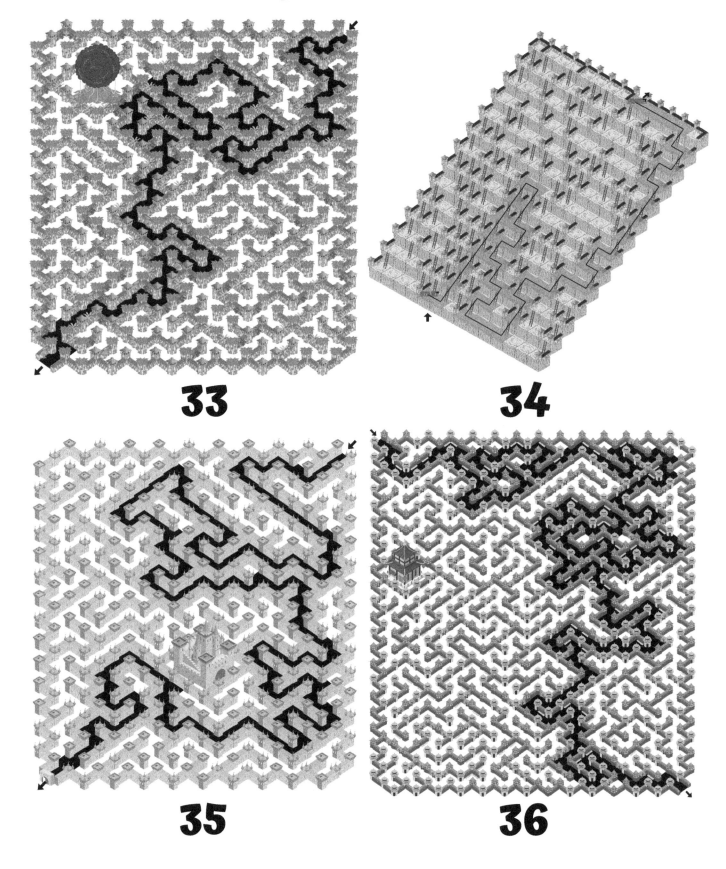

33

34

35

36

We hope you loved the mazes. If you did, would you consider posting an online review?

This helps us to continue providing great products, and helps potential buyers to make confident decisions.

For more mazes, find our similar titles

CPSIA information can be obtained
at www.ICGtesting.com
Printed in the USA
LVHW061018231120
672437LV00033BA/504